M. C. ESCHER®

2011 ENGAGEMENT CALENDAR

Pomegranate

Catalog No. H245

Published by Pomegranate Communications, Inc.
Box 808022, Petaluma CA 94975

Available in the UK and mainland Europe from Pomegranate Europe Ltd.
Unit 1, Heathcote Business Centre, Hurlbutt Road, Warwick, Warwickshire CV34 6TD, UK

Pomegranate also publishes M. C. Escher's work in wall, mini wall, and 365-day tear-off
calendars for 2011 as well as in jigsaw puzzles, notecards, journals, an address book, postcards,
magnets, mousepads, a stationery set, bookmarks, and the boxed gift *M. C. Escher Kaleidocycles*.
Other products and publications in our extensive line include a wide variety of calendars in
several formats for 2011, books, notepads, coloring books, posters, invitations, thank you cards,
Knowledge Cards®, birthday books, gift enclosures, and designer gift wrap.
For more information or to place an order, please contact
Pomegranate Communications, Inc., 800 227 1428, www.pomegranate.com.

Front cover: *Drawing Hands*, 1948. Lithograph, 11⅛ x 13⅛ in.

Designed by Oky Sulistio

Dates in color indicate US federal holidays.
Dates listed for all astronomical events in this calendar are based on Coordinated Universal Time (UTC),
the worldwide system of civil timekeeping. UTC is essentially equivalent to Greenwich Mean Time.
Moon phases and American, Canadian, and UK holidays are noted.

 NEW MOON   FIRST QUARTER   FULL MOON   LAST QUARTER

In his youth, M. C. Escher (Dutch, 1898–1972) drew what he observed. After attending the School for Architecture and Decorative Arts in Haarlem, Escher moved with his wife to Rome, whence he wandered every spring to the Italian countryside in search of subjects, covering long distances in the rough terrain by foot. These trips provided material for his graphic prints until 1937, when his work underwent a drastic change. Now spending most of his time in the studio, Escher made voyages into the imagination. His art no longer represented a tangible reality, but the inventions of his own mind. Escher's wildly ingenious new designs reflected the order and beauty he saw in a world that often seemed chaotic. Strangely logical manipulations of space, dimension, and perspective, Escher's works bind the surreal to the scientific, linking them in patterns of infinite repetition.

Escher's drawings and engravings reflect profound reverence for the underlying order of all things, while gently mocking our perception of reality. He challenged the hegemony of so-called natural laws with renderings of courtyards where "up" and "down" lose their meaning, of structures that flout gravity and perspective, of abstract patterns that gradually metamorphose into wriggling, flapping beasts. And yet his subjects, however impossible, always function according to their own elegant, impossible physical laws. There is order in Escher's universe.

2011

JANUARY

s	m	t	w	t	f	s
						1
2	3	4	5	6	7	8
9	10	11	12	13	14	15
16	17	18	19	20	21	22
23	24	25	26	27	28	29
30	31					

FEBRUARY

s	m	t	w	t	f	s
		1	2	3	4	5
6	7	8	9	10	11	12
13	14	15	16	17	18	19
20	21	22	23	24	25	26
27	28					

MARCH

s	m	t	w	t	f	s
		1	2	3	4	5
6	7	8	9	10	11	12
13	14	15	16	17	18	19
20	21	22	23	24	25	26
27	28	29	30	31		

APRIL

s	m	t	w	t	f	s
					1	2
3	4	5	6	7	8	9
10	11	12	13	14	15	16
17	18	19	20	21	22	23
24	25	26	27	28	29	30

MAY

s	m	t	w	t	f	s
1	2	3	4	5	6	7
8	9	10	11	12	13	14
15	16	17	18	19	20	21
22	23	24	25	26	27	28
29	30	31				

JUNE

s	m	t	w	t	f	s
			1	2	3	4
5	6	7	8	9	10	11
12	13	14	15	16	17	18
19	20	21	22	23	24	25
26	27	28	29	30		

2011

JULY

s	m	t	w	t	f	s
					1	2
3	4	5	6	7	8	9
10	11	12	13	14	15	16
17	18	19	20	21	22	23
24	25	26	27	28	29	30
31						

AUGUST

s	m	t	w	t	f	s
	1	2	3	4	5	6
7	8	9	10	11	12	13
14	15	16	17	18	19	20
21	22	23	24	25	26	27
28	29	30	31			

SEPTEMBER

s	m	t	w	t	f	s
				1	2	3
4	5	6	7	8	9	10
11	12	13	14	15	16	17
18	19	20	21	22	23	24
25	26	27	28	29	30	

OCTOBER

s	m	t	w	t	f	s
						1
2	3	4	5	6	7	8
9	10	11	12	13	14	15
16	17	18	19	20	21	22
23	24	25	26	27	28	29
30	31					

NOVEMBER

s	m	t	w	t	f	s
		1	2	3	4	5
6	7	8	9	10	11	12
13	14	15	16	17	18	19
20	21	22	23	24	25	26
27	28	29	30			

DECEMBER

s	m	t	w	t	f	s
				1	2	3
4	5	6	7	8	9	10
11	12	13	14	15	16	17
18	19	20	21	22	23	24
25	26	27	28	29	30	31

M. C. Escher (Dutch, 1898–1972)
Symmetry Drawing 91, 1953
India ink and watercolor, 7⁷⁄₁₆ x 7⁵⁄₈ in.

JANUARY

SUNDAY	MONDAY	TUESDAY	WEDNESDAY	THURSDAY	FRIDAY	SATURDAY
						1
2	3	4 ●	5	6	7	8
9	10	11	12 ◐	13	14	15
16	17	18	19 ○	20	21	22
23	24	25	26 ◑	27	28	29
30	31					

JAN 1   NEW YEAR'S DAY

JAN 3   BANK HOLIDAY (CANADA, UK)

JAN 4   BANK HOLIDAY (SCOTLAND)

JAN 17 MARTIN LUTHER KING JR. DAY

DEC / JAN

361 **27**   BANK HOLIDAY (UK)

362 **28** ☽   BANK HOLIDAY (UK)

363 **29**

364 **30**

365 **31**   NEW YEAR'S DAY HOLIDAY

1 **1**   NEW YEAR'S DAY

2 **2**

JANUARY

BANK HOLIDAY (CANADA, UK)

monday

3 ₃

BANK HOLIDAY (SCOTLAND)

tuesday

● 4 ₄

wednesday

5 ₅

thursday

6 ₆

friday

7 ₇

saturday

8 ₈

JANUARY

s	m	t	w	t	f	s
						1
2	3	4	5	6	7	8
9	10	11	12	13	14	15
16	17	18	19	20	21	22
23	24	25	26	27	28	29
30	31					

sunday

9 ₉

M. C. Escher (Dutch, 1898–1972)
Reptiles, 1943
Lithograph, 13⅛ x 15⅛ in.

JANUARY

tuesday
11 ₁₁

wednesday
◑ 12 ₁₂

thursday
13 ₁₃

friday
14 ₁₄

saturday
15 ₁₅

JANUARY

s	m	t	w	t	f	s
						1
2	3	4	5	6	7	8
9	10	11	12	13	14	15
16	17	18	19	20	21	22
23	24	25	26	27	28	29
30	31					

sunday
16 ₁₆

JANUARY

monday

17 17   MARTIN LUTHER KING JR. DAY

tuesday

18 18

wednesday

19 19 ○

thursday

20 20

friday

21 21

saturday

22 22

sunday

23 23

JANUARY

monday

24 ₂₄

tuesday

25 ₂₅

wednesday

◗ ## 26 ₂₆

thursday

27 ₂₇

friday

28 ₂₈

saturday

29 ₂₉

JANUARY

s	m	t	w	t	f	s
						1
2	3	4	5	6	7	8
9	10	11	12	13	14	15
16	17	18	19	20	21	22
23	24	25	26	27	28	29
30	31					

sunday

30 ₃₀

M. C. Escher (Dutch, 1898–1972)
Symmetry Drawing 3, 1936
Pencil and watercolor, 13 x 9⁹⁄₁₆ in.

FEBRUARY

SUNDAY	MONDAY	TUESDAY	WEDNESDAY	THURSDAY	FRIDAY	SATURDAY
		1	2	3 ●	4	5
6	7	8	9	10	11 ◐	12
13	14	15	16	17	18 ○	19
20	21	22	23	24 ◑	25	26
27	28					

FEB 3   LUNAR NEW YEAR   FEB 21   PRESIDENTS' DAY

FEB 14   VALENTINE'S DAY

JAN / FEB

monday

31
31

tuesday

32
1

wednesday

33
2

thursday   LUNAR NEW YEAR

34
3 ●

friday

35
4

saturday

36
5

sunday

37
6

FEBRUARY

monday

7 38

tuesday

8 39

wednesday

9 40

thursday

10 41

friday

◑ 11 42

saturday

12 43

FEBRUARY

s	m	t	w	t	f	s
		1	2	3	4	5
6	7	8	9	10	11	12
13	14	15	16	17	18	19
20	21	22	23	24	25	26
27	28					

sunday

13 44

M. C. Escher (Dutch, 1898–1972)
Castle in the Air, 1928
Woodcut, 24⅝ x 15¼ in.

FEBRUARY

VALENTINE'S DAY

monday

14 45

tuesday

15 46

wednesday

16 47

thursday

17 48

friday

○ # 18 49

saturday

19 50

FEBRUARY

s	m	t	w	t	f	s
		1	2	3	4	5
6	7	8	9	10	11	12
13	14	15	16	17	18	19
20	21	22	23	24	25	26
27	28					

sunday

20 51

M. C. Escher (Dutch, 1898–1972)
Circle Limit III, 1959
Woodcut, second state, in yellow, green, blue, brown, and black, printed from five blocks,
16⅜ in. diameter

FEBRUARY

PRESIDENTS' DAY

monday

21 52

tuesday

22 53

wednesday

23 54

thursday

◑ 24 55

friday

25 56

saturday

26 57

FEBRUARY

s	m	t	w	t	f	s
		1	2	3	4	5
6	7	8	9	10	11	12
13	14	15	16	17	18	19
20	21	22	23	24	25	26
27	28					

sunday

27 58

FEB / MAR

monday

59 **28**

tuesday

60 **1**

wednesday

61 **2**

thursday

62 **3**

friday

63 **4** ●

saturday

64 **5**

sunday

65 **6**

MARCH

SUNDAY	MONDAY	TUESDAY	WEDNESDAY	THURSDAY	FRIDAY	SATURDAY
		1	2	3	4 ●	5
6	7	8	9	10	11	12 ◐
13	14	15	16	17	18	19 ○
20	21	22	23	24	25	26 ◑
27	28	29	30	31		

MAR 8	MARDI GRAS	MAR 17	ST. PATRICK'S DAY
	INTERNATIONAL WOMEN'S DAY	MAR 19	PURIM (BEGINS AT SUNSET)
MAR 9	ASH WEDNESDAY	MAR 20	VERNAL EQUINOX 23:21 UTC
MAR 13	DAYLIGHT SAVING TIME BEGINS	MAR 27	SUMMER TIME BEGINS (UK)

M. C. Escher (Dutch, 1898–1972)
Symmetry Drawing 105, 1959
India ink, pencil, and watercolor, 8¹⁄₁₆ x 8¹⁄₁₆ in.

MARCH

monday

7 ₆₆

MARDI GRAS
INTERNATIONAL WOMEN'S DAY

tuesday

8 ₆₇

ASH WEDNESDAY

wednesday

9 ₆₈

---

thursday

10 ₆₉

---

friday

11 ₇₀

---

saturday

 12 ₇₁

MARCH

s	m	t	w	t	f	s
		1	2	3	4	5
6	7	8	9	10	11	12
13	14	15	16	17	18	19
20	21	22	23	24	25	26
27	28	29	30	31		

DAYLIGHT SAVING TIME BEGINS

sunday

13 ₇₂

M. C. Escher (Dutch, 1898–1972)
Three Worlds, 1955
Lithograph, 14¼ x 9¾ in.

monday

14 ₇₃

tuesday

15 ₇₄

wednesday

16 ₇₅

ST. PATRICK'S DAY

thursday

17 ₇₆

friday

18 ₇₇

PURIM (BEGINS AT SUNSET)

saturday

○ ## 19 ₇₈

MARCH

s	m	t	w	t	f	s
		1	2	3	4	5
6	7	8	9	10	11	12
13	14	15	16	17	18	19
20	21	22	23	24	25	26
27	28	29	30	31		

VERNAL EQUINOX 23:21 UTC

sunday

20 ₇₉

MARCH

monday

80 21

tuesday

81 22

wednesday

82 23

thursday

83 24

friday

84 25

saturday

85 26 ◑

sunday   SUMMER TIME BEGINS (UK)

86 27

monday

28 ₈₇

tuesday

29 ₈₈

wednesday

30 ₈₉

thursday

31 ₉₀

friday

1 ₉₁

saturday

2 ₉₂

APRIL

s	m	t	w	t	f	s
					1	2
3	4	5	6	7	8	9
10	11	12	13	14	15	16
17	18	19	20	21	22	23
24	25	26	27	28	29	30

MOTHERING SUNDAY (UK)

sunday

 3 ₉₃

M. C. Escher (Dutch, 1898–1972)
Fish and Scales, 1959
Woodcut, 14⅞ x 14⅞ in.

APRIL

SUNDAY	MONDAY	TUESDAY	WEDNESDAY	THURSDAY	FRIDAY	SATURDAY
					1	2
3 ●	4	5	6	7	8	9
10	11 ◐	12	13	14	15	16
17	18 ○	19	20	21	22	23
24	25 ◑	26	27	28	29	30

APR 3	MOTHERING SUNDAY (UK)	APR 22	BANK HOLIDAY (CANADA, UK)
APR 17	PALM SUNDAY		EARTH DAY
APR 18	PASSOVER (BEGINS AT SUNSET)	APR 24	EASTER
APR 22	GOOD FRIDAY	APR 25	EASTER MONDAY (CANADA, UK EXCEPT SCOTLAND)

M. C. Escher (Dutch, 1898–1972)
Ancona, 1936
Woodcut, 12¼ x 9½ in.

monday

4 94

tuesday

5 95

wednesday

6 96

thursday

7 97

friday

8 98

saturday

9 99

APRIL

s	m	t	w	t	f	s
					1	2
3	4	5	6	7	8	9
10	11	12	13	14	15	16
17	18	19	20	21	22	23
24	25	26	27	28	29	30

sunday

10 100

APRIL

monday
101 **11** ◑

tuesday
102 **12**

wednesday
103 **13**

thursday
104 **14**

friday
105 **15**

saturday
106 **16**

sunday   PALM SUNDAY
107 **17**

APRIL

PASSOVER (BEGINS AT SUNSET)

monday

○ 18 108

tuesday

19 109

wednesday

20 110

thursday

21 111

GOOD FRIDAY
BANK HOLIDAY (CANADA, UK)
EARTH DAY

friday

22 112

saturday

23 113

APRIL

s	m	t	w	t	f	s
					1	2
3	4	5	6	7	8	9
10	11	12	13	14	15	16
17	18	19	20	21	22	23
24	25	26	27	28	29	30

EASTER

sunday

24 114

M. C. Escher (Dutch, 1898–1972)
Phosphorescent Sea, 1933
Lithograph, 12⅞ x 9⅝ in.

EASTER MONDAY (CANADA, UK EXCEPT SCOTLAND)

monday
◑ 25 115

tuesday
26 116

wednesday
27 117

thursday
28 118

friday
29 119

saturday
30 120

MAY

s	m	t	w	t	f	s
1	2	3	4	5	6	7
8	9	10	11	12	13	14
15	16	17	18	19	20	21
22	23	24	25	26	27	28
29	30	31				

sunday
1 121

M. C. Escher (Dutch, 1898–1972)
Symmetry Drawing 54, 1942
India ink, colored ink, colored pencil, and watercolor, 8¹¹⁄₁₆ x 8⅛ in.

MAY

SUNDAY	MONDAY	TUESDAY	WEDNESDAY	THURSDAY	FRIDAY	SATURDAY
1	2	3 ●	4	5	6	7
8	9	10 ◐	11	12	13	14
15	16	17 ○	18	19	20	21
22	23	24 ◑	25	26	27	28
29	30	31				

MAY 2	BANK HOLIDAY (UK)		MAY 21	ARMED FORCES DAY
MAY 5	CINCO DE MAYO		MAY 23	VICTORIA DAY (CANADA)
MAY 8	MOTHER'S DAY		MAY 30	MEMORIAL DAY
				BANK HOLIDAY (UK)

M. C. Escher (Dutch, 1898–1972)
Butterflies, 1950
Wood engraving, 11⅛ x 10¼ in.

MAY

BANK HOLIDAY (UK)   *monday*

                                                                    2 122

                                                                    tuesday

                                                                ● 3 123

                                                                    wednesday

                                                                    4 124

CINCO DE MAYO   *thursday*

                                                                    5 125

                                                                    friday

                                                                    6 126

                                                                    saturday

                                                                    7 127

MAY

s	m	t	w	t	f	s
1	2	3	4	5	6	7
8	9	10	11	12	13	14
15	16	17	18	19	20	21
22	23	24	25	26	27	28
29	30	31				

MOTHER'S DAY   *sunday*

                                                                    8 128

MAY

monday
129
9

tuesday
130
10 ◑

wednesday
131
11

thursday
132
12

friday
133
13

saturday
134
14

sunday
135
15

MAY

tuesday

○ 17 ₁₃₇

wednesday

18 ₁₃₈

thursday

19 ₁₃₉

friday

20 ₁₄₀

ARMED FORCES DAY

saturday

21 ₁₄₁

MAY

s	m	t	w	t	f	s
1	2	3	4	5	6	7
8	9	10	11	12	13	14
15	16	17	18	19	20	21
22	23	24	25	26	27	28
29	30	31				

sunday

22 ₁₄₂

M. C. Escher (Dutch, 1898–1972)
Waterfall, 1961
Lithograph, 15 x 11¾ in.

VICTORIA DAY (CANADA)

monday

23 143

tuesday

◐ 24 144

wednesday

25 145

thursday

26 146

friday

27 147

saturday

28 148

MAY

s	m	t	w	t	f	s
1	2	3	4	5	6	7
8	9	10	11	12	13	14
15	16	17	18	19	20	21
22	23	24	25	26	27	28
29	30	31				

sunday

29 149

MAY / JUN

monday

150 30

tuesday

151 31

wednesday

152 1 ●

thursday

153 2

friday

154 3

saturday

155 4

sunday

156 5

JUNE

SUNDAY	MONDAY	TUESDAY	WEDNESDAY	THURSDAY	FRIDAY	SATURDAY
			1 ●	2	3	4
5	6	7	8	9 ◑	10	11
12	13	14	15 ○	16	17	18
19	20	21	22	23 ◐	24	25
26	27	28	29	30		

JUN 14   FLAG DAY   JUN 21   SUMMER SOLSTICE 17:16 UTC

JUN 19   FATHER'S DAY

M. C. Escher (Dutch, 1898–1972)
Self-Portrait, 1923
Woodcut, 12¾ x 6¼ in.

monday

6 ₁₅₇

tuesday

7 ₁₅₈

wednesday

8 ₁₅₉

thursday

◐ 9 ₁₆₀

friday

10 ₁₆₁

saturday

11 ₁₆₂

JUNE

s	m	t	w	t	f	s
			1	2	3	4
5	6	7	8	9	10	11
12	13	14	15	16	17	18
19	20	21	22	23	24	25
26	27	28	29	30		

sunday

12 ₁₆₃

JUNE

monday

13

tuesday

FLAG DAY

14

wednesday

15 ○

thursday

16

friday

17

saturday

18

sunday

FATHER'S DAY

19

JUNE

monday
20 171

SUMMER SOLSTICE 17:16 UTC

tuesday
21 172

wednesday
22 173

thursday
◑ 23 174

friday
24 175

saturday
25 176

JUNE

s	m	t	w	t	f	s
			1	2	3	4
5	6	7	8	9	10	11
12	13	14	15	16	17	18
19	20	21	22	23	24	25
26	27	28	29	30		

sunday
26 177

M. C. Escher (Dutch, 1898–1972)
Dragon, 1952
Wood engraving, 12⅝ x 9½ in.

monday

27 178

tuesday

28 179

wednesday

29 180

thursday

30 181

CANADA DAY (CANADA)

friday

● 1 182

saturday

2 183

JULY

s	m	t	w	t	f	s
					1	2
3	4	5	6	7	8	9
10	11	12	13	14	15	16
17	18	19	20	21	22	23
24	25	26	27	28	29	30
31						

sunday

3 184

M. C. Escher (Dutch, 1898–1972)
Symmetry Drawing 72, 1948
Colored pencil and ink, 10½ x 7⅞ in.

JULY

SUNDAY	MONDAY	TUESDAY	WEDNESDAY	THURSDAY	FRIDAY	SATURDAY
					1 ●	2
3	4	5	6	7	8 ◐	9
10	11	12	13	14	15 ○	16
17	18	19	20	21	22	23 ◑
24	25	26	27	28	29	30 ●
31						

JUL 1   CANADA DAY (CANADA)   JUL 12   BANK HOLIDAY (N. IRELAND)

JUL 4   INDEPENDENCE DAY

M. C. Escher (Dutch, 1898–1972)
Still Life and Street, 1937
Woodcut, 19⅛ x 19¼ in.

JULY

INDEPENDENCE DAY

monday

4 ₁₈₅

tuesday

5 ₁₈₆

wednesday

6 ₁₈₇

thursday

7 ₁₈₈

friday

◑ 8 ₁₈₉

saturday

9 ₁₉₀

JULY

s	m	t	w	t	f	s
					1	2
3	4	5	6	7	8	9
10	11	12	13	14	15	16
17	18	19	20	21	22	23
24	25	26	27	28	29	30
31						

sunday

10 ₁₉₁

JULY

192

monday

11

tuesday

BANK HOLIDAY (N. IRELAND)

193

12

wednesday

194

13

thursday

195

14

friday

196

15 ○

saturday

197

16

sunday

198

17

JULY

monday

18 199

tuesday

19 200

wednesday

20 201

thursday

21 202

friday

22 203

saturday

◑ 23 204

JULY

s	m	t	w	t	f	s
					1	2
3	4	5	6	7	8	9
10	11	12	13	14	15	16
17	18	19	20	21	22	23
24	25	26	27	28	29	30
31						

sunday

24 205

M. C. Escher (Dutch, 1898–1972)
Sky and Water II, 1938
Woodcut, 24½ x 16 in.

JULY

monday
25 <small>206</small>

tuesday
26 <small>207</small>

wednesday
27 <small>208</small>

thursday
28 <small>209</small>

friday
29 <small>210</small>

saturday
● 30 <small>211</small>

sunday
31 <small>212</small>

JULY

s	m	t	w	t	f	s
					1	2
3	4	5	6	7	8	9
10	11	12	13	14	15	16
17	18	19	20	21	22	23
24	25	26	27	28	29	30
31						

M. C. Escher (Dutch, 1898–1972)
Symmetry Drawing 31, 1940
Pencil and watercolor, 13⁵⁄₁₆ x 9⅝ in.

AUGUST

SUNDAY	MONDAY	TUESDAY	WEDNESDAY	THURSDAY	FRIDAY	SATURDAY
	1	2	3	4	5	6 ◐
7	8	9	10	11	12	13 ○
14	15	16	17	18	19	20
21 ◑	22	23	24	25	26	27
28	29 ●	30	31			

AUG 1   CIVIC HOLIDAY (CANADA, MOST PROVINCES)

BANK HOLIDAY (SCOTLAND)

AUG 29   BANK HOLIDAY (UK EXCEPT SCOTLAND)

AUGUST

monday

213

1

CIVIC HOLIDAY (CANADA, MOST PROVINCES)
BANK HOLIDAY (SCOTLAND)

tuesday

214

2

wednesday

215

3

thursday

216

4

friday

217

5

saturday

218

6 ◑

sunday

219

7

AUGUST

monday

8 220

tuesday

9 221

wednesday

10 222

thursday

11 223

friday

12 224

saturday

○ 13 225

AUGUST

s	m	t	w	t	f	s
	1	2	3	4	5	6
7	8	9	10	11	12	13
14	15	16	17	18	19	20
21	22	23	24	25	26	27
28	29	30	31			

sunday

14 226

M. C. Escher (Dutch, 1898–1972)
Three Spheres II, 1946
Lithograph, 10⅝ x 18¼ in.

AUGUST

monday

15 227

tuesday

16 228

wednesday

17 229

thursday

18 230

friday

19 231

saturday

20 232

AUGUST

s	m	t	w	t	f	s
	1	2	3	4	5	6
7	8	9	10	11	12	13
14	15	16	17	18	19	20
21	22	23	24	25	26	27
28	29	30	31			

sunday

◐ 21 233

AUGUST

monday
22

tuesday
23

wednesday
24

thursday
25

friday
26

saturday
27

sunday
28

BANK HOLIDAY (UK EXCEPT SCOTLAND)

monday

● 29 ₂₄₁

tuesday

30 ₂₄₂

wednesday

31 ₂₄₃

thursday

1 ₂₄₄

friday

2 ₂₄₅

saturday

3 ₂₄₆

SEPTEMBER

s	m	t	w	t	f	s
				1	2	3
4	5	6	7	8	9	10
11	12	13	14	15	16	17
18	19	20	21	22	23	24
25	26	27	28	29	30	

sunday

◐ 4 ₂₄₇

M. C. Escher (Dutch, 1898–1972)
Symmetry Drawing 115, 1963
Ink and watercolor, 7⅞ x 7⅞ in.

SEPTEMBER

SUNDAY	MONDAY	TUESDAY	WEDNESDAY	THURSDAY	FRIDAY	SATURDAY
				1	2	3
4 ◐	5	6	7	8	9	10
11	12 ○	13	14	15	16	17
18	19	20 ◑	21	22	23	24
25	26	27 ●	28	29	30	

SEP 5	LABOR DAY (US, CANADA)	SEP 23	AUTUMNAL EQUINOX 09:04 UTC
SEP 21	INTERNATIONAL DAY OF PEACE	SEP 28	ROSH HASHANAH (BEGINS AT SUNSET)

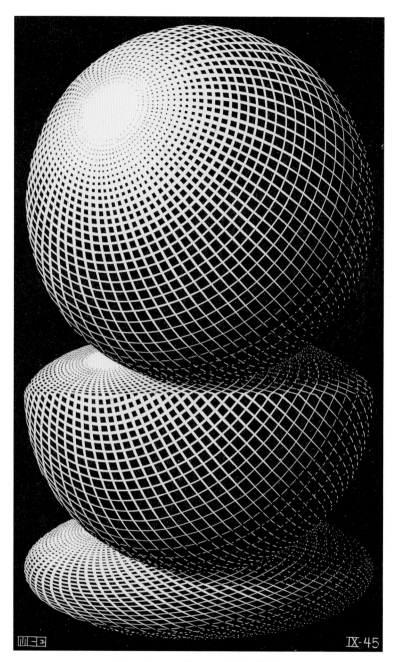

M. C. Escher (Dutch, 1898–1972)
Three Spheres I, 1945
Wood engraving, 11 x 6⅝ in.

SEPTEMBER

LABOR DAY (US, CANADA)

monday

5 248

tuesday

6 249

wednesday

7 250

thursday

8 251

friday

9 252

saturday

10 253

SEPTEMBER

s	m	t	w	t	f	s
				1	2	3
4	5	6	7	8	9	10
11	12	13	14	15	16	17
18	19	20	21	22	23	24
25	26	27	28	29	30	

sunday

11 254

SEPTEMBER

monday

255 12 ○

tuesday

256 13

wednesday

257 14

thursday

258 15

friday

259 16

saturday

260 17

sunday

261 18

SEPTEMBER

monday

19 ₂₆₂

tuesday

◐ ## 20 ₂₆₃

INTERNATIONAL DAY OF PEACE

wednesday

21 ₂₆₄

thursday

22 ₂₆₅

AUTUMNAL EQUINOX 09:04 UTC

friday

23 ₂₆₆

saturday

24 ₂₆₇

SEPTEMBER

s	m	t	w	t	f	s
				1	2	3
4	5	6	7	8	9	10
11	12	13	14	15	16	17
18	19	20	21	22	23	24
25	26	27	28	29	30	

sunday

25 ₂₆₈

M. C. Escher (Dutch, 1898–1972)
The Sixth Day of the Creation, 1926
Woodcut, 14¾ x 11 in.

monday
26 ₂₆₉

tuesday
● 27 ₂₇₀

ROSH HASHANAH (BEGINS AT SUNSET)

wednesday
28 ₂₇₁

thursday
29 ₂₇₂

friday
30 ₂₇₃

saturday
1 ₂₇₄

OCTOBER

s	m	t	w	t	f	s
						1
2	3	4	5	6	7	8
9	10	11	12	13	14	15
16	17	18	19	20	21	22
23	24	25	26	27	28	29
30	31					

sunday
2 ₂₇₅

M. C. Escher (Dutch, 1898–1972)
Whirlpools, 1957
Wood engraving and woodcut, second state, in red, gray, and black,
printed from two blocks, 17¼ x 9¼ in.

OCTOBER

SUNDAY	MONDAY	TUESDAY	WEDNESDAY	THURSDAY	FRIDAY	SATURDAY
						1
2	3	4 ◑	5	6	7	8
9	10	11	12 ○	13	14	15
16	17	18	19	20 ◑	21	22
23	24	25	26 ●	27	28	29
30	31					

OCT 7   YOM KIPPUR (BEGINS AT SUNSET)
OCT 10   COLUMBUS DAY
         THANKSGIVING DAY (CANADA)
OCT 24   UNITED NATIONS DAY
OCT 30   SUMMER TIME ENDS (UK)
OCT 31   HALLOWEEN

OCTOBER

monday

276 3

tuesday

277 4 ◑

wednesday

278 5

thursday

279 6

friday   YOM KIPPUR (BEGINS AT SUNSET)

280 7

saturday

281 8

sunday

282 9

OCTOBER

COLUMBUS DAY
THANKSGIVING DAY (CANADA)

monday

10 283

tuesday

11 284

wednesday

○ 12 285

thursday

13 286

friday

14 287

saturday

15 288

OCTOBER

s	m	t	w	t	f	s
						1
2	3	4	5	6	7	8
9	10	11	12	13	14	15
16	17	18	19	20	21	22
23	24	25	26	27	28	29
30	31					

sunday

16 289

M. C. Escher (Dutch, 1898–1972)
Day and Night, 1938
Woodcut in black and gray, printed from two blocks, 15⅜ x 26⅝ in.

OCTOBER

tuesday

18 ₂₉₁

wednesday

19 ₂₉₂

thursday

◑ 20 ₂₉₃

friday

21 ₂₉₄

saturday

22 ₂₉₅

OCTOBER

s	m	t	w	t	f	s
						1
2	3	4	5	6	7	8
9	10	11	12	13	14	15
16	17	18	19	20	21	22
23	24	25	26	27	28	29
30	31					

sunday

23 ₂₉₆

M. C. Escher (Dutch, 1898–1972)
Libellula (Dragonfly), 1936
Wood engraving, 8¼ x 11 in.

OCTOBER

UNITED NATIONS DAY

monday

24 ₂₉₇

tuesday

25 ₂₉₈

wednesday

● ## 26 ₂₉₉

thursday

27 ₃₀₀

friday

28 ₃₀₁

saturday

29 ₃₀₂

OCTOBER

s	m	t	w	t	f	s
						1
2	3	4	5	6	7	8
9	10	11	12	13	14	15
16	17	18	19	20	21	22
23	24	25	26	27	28	29
30	31					

SUMMER TIME ENDS (UK)

sunday

30 ₃₀₃

M. C. Escher (Dutch, 1898–1972)
Regular Division of the Plane III, 1957
Woodcut in red, 9½ x 7⅛ in.

NOVEMBER

SUNDAY	MONDAY	TUESDAY	WEDNESDAY	THURSDAY	FRIDAY	SATURDAY
		1	2 ◑	3	4	5
6	7	8	9	10 ○	11	12
13	14	15	16	17	18 ◐	19
20	21	22	23	24	25 ●	26
27	28	29	30			

NOV 6   DAYLIGHT SAVING TIME ENDS

NOV 11   VETERANS DAY
         REMEMBRANCE DAY (CANADA)

NOV 24   THANKSGIVING

NOV 30   ST. ANDREW'S DAY (SCOTLAND)

OCT / NOV

HALLOWEEN

304 31

305 1

306 2 ◑

307 3

308 4

309 5

DAYLIGHT SAVING TIME ENDS

310 6

NOVEMBER

VETERANS DAY
REMEMBRANCE DAY (CANADA)

NOVEMBER

s	m	t	w	t	f	s
			1	2	3	4	5
6	7	8	9	10	11	12
13	14	15	16	17	18	19
20	21	22	23	24	25	26
27	28	29	30			

M. C. Escher (Dutch, 1898–1972)
Still Life with Mirror, 1934
Lithograph, 15½ x 11¼ in.

NOVEMBER

monday

14 ₃₁₈

tuesday

15 ₃₁₉

wednesday

16 ₃₂₀

thursday

17 ₃₂₁

friday

◑ ## 18 ₃₂₂

saturday

19 ₃₂₃

NOVEMBER

s	m	t	w	t	f	s
			1	2	3	4	5
6	7	8	9	10	11	12
13	14	15	16	17	18	19
20	21	22	23	24	25	26
27	28	29	30			

sunday

20 ₃₂₄

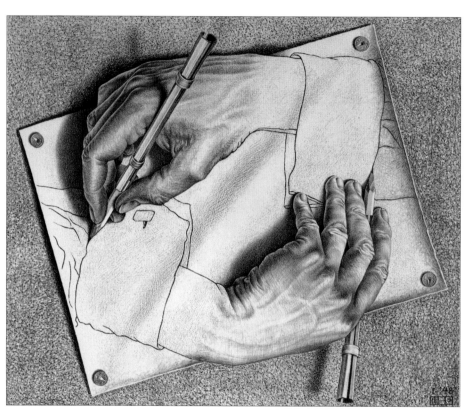

M. C. Escher (Dutch, 1898–1972)
Drawing Hands, 1948
Lithograph, 11⅛ x 13⅛ in.

NOVEMBER

monday
21 <small>325</small>

tuesday
22 <small>326</small>

wednesday
23 <small>327</small>

THANKSGIVING

thursday
24 <small>328</small>

friday
● 25 <small>329</small>

saturday
26 <small>330</small>

NOVEMBER

s	m	t	w	t	f	s
		1	2	3	4	5
6	7	8	9	10	11	12
13	14	15	16	17	18	19
20	21	22	23	24	25	26
27	28	29	30			

sunday
27 <small>331</small>

NOV / DEC

monday

332 28

tuesday

333 29

wednesday   ST. ANDREW'S DAY (SCOTLAND)

334 30

thursday

335 1

friday

336 2 ◑

saturday

337 3

sunday

338 4

DECEMBER

SUNDAY	MONDAY	TUESDAY	WEDNESDAY	THURSDAY	FRIDAY	SATURDAY
				1	2 ◑	3
4	5	6	7	8	9	10 ○
11	12	13	14	15	16	17
18 ◐	19	20	21	22	23	24 ●
25	26	27	28	29	30	31

DEC 20	HANUKKAH (BEGINS AT SUNSET)	DEC 26	CHRISTMAS HOLIDAY
DEC 22	WINTER SOLSTICE 05:30 UTC		KWANZAA BEGINS
DEC 25	CHRISTMAS		BOXING DAY (CANADA, UK)
		DEC 27	BANK HOLIDAY (UK)

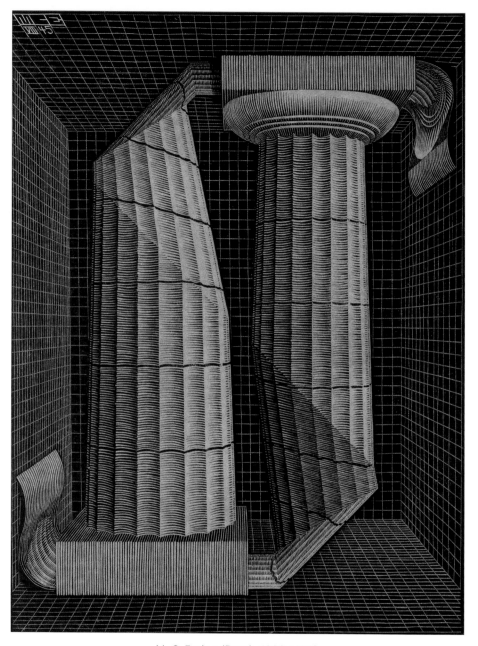

M. C. Escher (Dutch, 1898–1972)
(Two) Doric Columns, 1945
Wood engraving in black, brown, and blue-green, printed from three blocks, 12⅛ x 9½ in.

DECEMBER

monday

5 339

tuesday

6 340

wednesday

7 341

thursday

8 342

friday

9 343

saturday

○ 10 344

DECEMBER

s	m	t	w	t	f	s
				1	2	3
4	5	6	7	8	9	10
11	12	13	14	15	16	17
18	19	20	21	22	23	24
25	26	27	28	29	30	31

sunday

11 345

M. C. Escher (Dutch, 1898–1972)
Fireworks, 1933
Lithograph, 16¾ x 8⅞ in.

DECEMBER

DECEMBER

s	m	t	w	t	f	s
				1	2	3
4	5	6	7	8	9	10
11	12	13	14	15	16	17
18	19	20	21	22	23	24
25	26	27	28	29	30	31

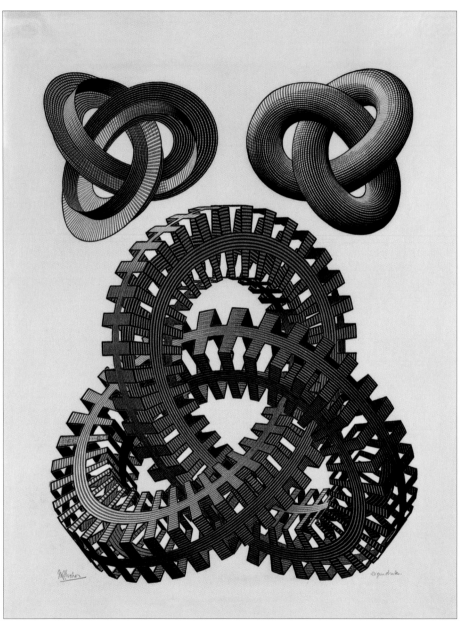

M. C. Escher (Dutch, 1898–1972)
Knots, 1965
Woodcut in black, green, and brown, printed from three blocks, 16⅞ x 12⅝ in.

DECEMBER

HANUKKAH (BEGINS AT SUNSET)

WINTER SOLSTICE 05:30 UTC

DECEMBER

s	m	t	w	t	f	s
				1	2	3
4	5	6	7	8	9	10
11	12	13	14	15	16	17
18	19	20	21	22	23	24
25	26	27	28	29	30	31

CHRISTMAS

DEC / JAN

monday
26

CHRISTMAS HOLIDAY
KWANZAA BEGINS
BOXING DAY (CANADA, UK)

tuesday
27

BANK HOLIDAY (UK)

wednesday
28

thursday
29

friday
30

saturday
31

sunday
1 ◑

NEW YEAR'S DAY

JANUARY 2012

SUNDAY	MONDAY	TUESDAY	WEDNESDAY	THURSDAY	FRIDAY	SATURDAY
1 ◐	2	3	4	5	6	7
8	9 ○	10	11	12	13	14
15	16 ◑	17	18	19	20	21
22	23 ●	24	25	26	27	28
29	30	31 ◐				

JAN	1	NEW YEAR'S DAY	JAN 3	BANK HOLIDAY (SCOTLAND)
JAN	2	NEW YEAR'S DAY HOLIDAY	JAN 16	MARTIN LUTHER KING JR. DAY
		BANK HOLIDAY (CANADA, UK)	JAN 23	LUNAR NEW YEAR

JANUARY 2012

monday

2 2

NEW YEAR'S DAY HOLIDAY
BANK HOLIDAY (CANADA, UK)

tuesday

3 3

BANK HOLIDAY (SCOTLAND)

wednesday

4 4

thursday

5 5

friday

6 6

saturday

7 7

sunday

8 8

JANUARY 2012

monday

○ **9** 9

tuesday

10 10

wednesday

11 11

thursday

12 12

friday

13 13

saturday

14 14

JANUARY

s	m	t	w	t	f	s
1	2	3	4	5	6	7
8	9	10	11	12	13	14
15	16	17	18	19	20	21
22	23	24	25	26	27	28
29	30	31				

sunday

15 15

JANUARY 2012

monday   MARTIN LUTHER KING JR. DAY

16   16 ◑

---

tuesday

17   17

---

wednesday

18   18

---

thursday

19   19

---

friday

20   20

---

saturday

21   21

---

sunday

22   22

JANUARY 2012

LUNAR NEW YEAR

monday
● 23 ₂₃

tuesday
24 ₂₄

wednesday
25 ₂₅

thursday
26 ₂₆

friday
27 ₂₇

saturday
28 ₂₈

JANUARY

s	m	t	w	t	f	s
1	2	3	4	5	6	7
8	9	10	11	12	13	14
15	16	17	18	19	20	21
22	23	24	25	26	27	28
29	30	31				

sunday
29 ₂₉

2011 INTERNATIONAL HOLIDAYS

Following are the dates of major holidays in 2011 for selected countries. Islamic observances are subject to adjustment. Holidays of the United States, the United Kingdom, and Canada, and major Jewish holidays, appear on this calendar's grid pages. Pomegranate is not responsible for errors or omissions in this list. All dates should be confirmed with local sources before making international travel or business plans. Please note: Most international holidays that fall on a weekend (or another holiday) are observed on the following Monday (or the next working day). This is not true, however, of Mexico, South Korea, or the Netherlands.

ARGENTINA

1	Jan	New Year's Day
24	Mar	National Day of Memory for Truth and Justice
2	Apr	Veterans Day (Malvinas War Memorial)
21	Apr	Holy Thursday
22	Apr	Good Friday
24	Apr	Easter
1	May	Labor Day
25	May	Revolution Day
20	Jun	Flag Day*
9	Jul	Independence Day
15	Aug	San Martín Day*
12	Oct	Día de la Diversidad Cultural Americana†
8	Dec	Immaculate Conception
25	Dec	Christmas

* Observed on third Monday of month
† Observed on second Monday of October

AUSTRALIA

1	Jan	New Year's Day
26	Jan	Australia Day
7	Mar	Labor Day (WA)
14	Mar	Labor Day (Vic)
		Eight Hours Day (Tas)
		Adelaide Cup (SA)
		Canberra Day (ACT)
22–25	Apr	Easter Holiday
26	Apr	ANZAC Day
		Easter Tuesday (Tas)
2	May	Labor Day (Qld)
		May Day (NT)
6	Jun	Foundation Day (WA)
13	Jun	Queen's Birthday (except WA)
		Volunteer's Day (SA)
1	Aug	Picnic Day (NT)
		Bank Holiday (NSW)
3	Oct	Queen's Birthday (WA)
		Labor Day (NSW, ACT, SA)
1	Nov	Melbourne Cup (Vic)
25	Dec	Christmas
26	Dec	Boxing Day (except SA)
		Christmas Holiday (SA)
27	Dec	Proclamation Day (SA)

BRAZIL

1	Jan	New Year's Day
20	Jan	São Sebastião Day (Rio de Janeiro)
25	Jan	São Paulo Anniversary (São Paulo)
7–8	Mar	Carnival
9	Mar	Ash Wednesday (until 2 pm)
21	Apr	Tiradentes Day
22	Apr	Good Friday
24	Apr	Easter
1	May	Labor Day
23	Jun	Corpus Christi
7	Sep	Independence Day
12	Oct	Our Lady of Aparecida

2	Nov	All Souls' Day
15	Nov	Proclamation of the Republic
25	Dec	Christmas

CHINA (SEE ALSO HONG KONG)

1	Jan	New Year's Day
2	Feb	Chinese New Year Holiday begins
8	Feb	Last Day of New Year Holiday
5	Apr	Tomb-Sweeping Day
1	May	Labor Day
6	Jun	Dragon Boat Festival
12	Sep	Mid-Autumn Festival
26 Sep–2 Oct		National Day Holiday

FRANCE

1	Jan	New Year's Day
24	Apr	Easter
25	Apr	Easter Monday
1	May	Labor Day
8	May	Victory in Europe Day
2	Jun	Ascension Day
12	Jun	Pentecost
13	Jun	Whit Monday
14	Jul	Bastille Day
15	Aug	Assumption
1	Nov	All Saints' Day
11	Nov	Armistice Day
25	Dec	Christmas

GERMANY

1	Jan	New Year's Day
22	Apr	Good Friday
24	Apr	Easter
25	Apr	Easter Monday
1	May	Labor Day
2	Jun	Ascension Day
12	Jun	Pentecost
13	Jun	Whit Monday
3	Oct	Unity Day
25	Dec	Christmas
26	Dec	St. Stephen's Day

HONG KONG

1	Jan	New Year's Day
3–5	Feb	Spring Festival / Lunar New Year
2–5	Apr	Easter Holiday
5	Apr	Tomb-Sweeping Day
22	Apr	Good Friday
23	Apr	Holy Saturday
24	Apr	Easter
25	Apr	Easter Monday
1	May	Labor Day
10	May	Buddha's Birthday
6	Jun	Dragon Boat Festival
1	Jul	Special Administrative Region Establishment Day
13	Sep	Day After Mid-Autumn Festival
1	Oct	National Day
5	Oct	Chung Yeung Festival
25	Dec	Christmas
26	Dec	Boxing Day

INDIA

1	Jan	New Year's Day
14	Jan	Makar Sankranti (North India)
15	Jan	Makar Sankranti (Bengal)
26	Jan	Republic Day
15	Feb	Prophet Muhammad's Birthday
16	Feb	Milad-un-Nabi
3	Mar	Maha Shivaratri
19	Mar	Holi
12	Apr	Ram Navami
14	Apr	Dr. B. R. Ambedkar's Birthday
16	Apr	Mahavir Jayanti
22	Apr	Good Friday
24	Apr	Easter
17	May	Buddha Purnima
15	Aug	Independence Day
21	Aug	Janamashtami
31	Aug	Ramzan-Eid (Eid al-Fitr)
2	Oct	Mahatma Gandhi's Birthday
26	Oct	Diwali (Deepavali)
7	Nov	Bakr-Eid (Eid al-Adha)
11	Nov	Guru Nanak's Birthday
6	Dec	Islamic New Year
25	Dec	Christmas

IRELAND

1	Jan	New Year's Day
17	Mar	St. Patrick's Day
22	Apr	Good Friday
24	Apr	Easter
25	Apr	Easter Monday
2	May	Bank Holiday
6	Jun	Bank Holiday
1	Aug	Bank Holiday
31	Oct	Bank Holiday
25	Dec	Christmas
26	Dec	St. Stephen's Day

ISRAEL

20	Mar	Purim (except Jerusalem)
21	Mar	Purim Bank Holiday (Jerusalem)
19	Apr	First Day of Pesach
25	Apr	Last Day of Pesach
1	May	Holocaust Memorial Day
9	May	National Memorial Day
10	May	Independence Day
8	Jun	Shavuot
9	Aug	Tisha B'Av
29–30	Sep	Rosh Hashanah
8	Oct	Yom Kippur
13	Oct	First Day of Sukkot
20	Oct	Shemini Atzeret / Simhat Torah

ITALY

1	Jan	New Year's Day
6	Jan	Epiphany
24	Apr	Easter
25	Apr	Easter Monday
		Liberation Day
1	May	Labor Day
2	Jun	Republic Day
29	Jun	Sts. Peter and Paul (Rome)

15	Aug	Assumption
1	Nov	All Saints' Day
8	Dec	Immaculate Conception
25	Dec	Christmas
26	Dec	St. Stephen's Day

JAPAN

1	Jan	New Year's Day
10	Jan	Coming of Age Day
11	Feb	National Foundation Day
21	Mar	Vernal Equinox
29	Apr	Shōwa Day
3	May	Constitution Memorial Day
4	May	Greenery Day
5	May	Children's Day
18	Jul	Marine Day
19	Sep	Respect for the Aged Day
23	Sep	Autumnal Equinox
10	Oct	Health and Sports Day
3	Nov	Culture Day
23	Nov	Labor Thanksgiving Day
23	Dec	Emperor's Birthday

MEXICO

1	Jan	New Year's Day
5	Feb	Constitution Day*
21	Mar	Benito Juárez Day†
21	Apr	Holy Thursday
22	Apr	Good Friday
24	Apr	Easter
1	May	Labor Day
16	Sep	Independence Day
1	Nov	All Saints' Day
2	Nov	All Souls' Day (Day of the Dead)
20	Nov	Revolution Day†
12	Dec	Our Lady of Guadalupe
25	Dec	Christmas

* Observed on first Monday of month
† Observed on third Monday of month

NETHERLANDS

1	Jan	New Year's Day
22	Apr	Good Friday
24	Apr	Easter
25	Apr	Easter Monday
30	Apr	Queen's Day
2	Jun	Ascension Day
12	Jun	Pentecost
13	Jun	Whit Monday
25-26	Dec	Christmas Holiday

NEW ZEALAND

1-2	Jan	New Year's Holiday
22	Jan	Provincial Anniversary (Wellington)*
29	Jan	Provincial Anniversary (Auckland)*
6	Feb	Waitangi Day
22	Apr	Good Friday
24	Apr	Easter
25	Apr	Easter Monday
		ANZAC Day
6	Jun	Queen's Birthday
24	Oct	Labor Day
11	Nov	Provincial Anniversary (Canterbury)
25	Dec	Christmas
26	Dec	Boxing Day

* Observed on closest Monday

PUERTO RICO

6	Jan	Three Kings Day (Epiphany)
11	Jan	Eugenio María de Hostos Day*
22	Mar	Emancipation Day
16	Apr	José de Diego Day†
22	Apr	Good Friday
24	Apr	Easter
17	Jul	Luis Muñoz Rivera Day†
25	Jul	Constitution Day
27	Jul	José Celso Barbosa Day
12	Oct	Día de la Raza*
19	Nov	Discovery of Puerto Rico
24	Dec	Christmas Eve

All US federal holidays also observed
* Observed on second Monday of month
† Observed on third Monday of month

RUSSIA

3	Jan	New Year's Holiday Begins
7	Jan	Orthodox Christmas
10	Jan	Last Day of New Year's Holiday
23	Feb	Defenders of the Fatherland Day
8	Mar	International Women's Day
24	Apr	Orthodox Easter
1	May	Spring and Labor Day
9	May	Victory Day
12	Jun	Independence Day
4	Nov	National Unity Day

SINGAPORE

1	Jan	New Year's Day
3-4	Feb	Chinese New Year Holiday
22	Apr	Good Friday
24	Apr	Easter
1	May	Labor Day
17	May	Vesak Day (Buddha's Birthday)
31	Jul	Beginning of Ramadan
9	Aug	National Day
29	Aug	Hari Raya Puasa (Eid al-Fitr)
26	Oct	Deepavali
5	Nov	Hari Raya Haji (Eid al-Adha)
25	Dec	Christmas

SOUTH AFRICA

1	Jan	New Year's Day
21	Mar	Human Rights Day
22	Apr	Good Friday
24	Apr	Easter
25	Apr	Family Day
27	Apr	Freedom Day
1	May	Workers' Day
16	Jun	Youth Day
9	Aug	National Women's Day
24	Sep	Heritage Day
16	Dec	Day of Reconciliation
25	Dec	Christmas
26	Dec	Day of Goodwill

SOUTH KOREA

1	Jan	New Year's Day
2-4	Feb	Lunar New Year Holiday
1	Mar	Independence Movement Day
5	May	Children's Day
10	May	Birth of Buddha
6	Jun	Memorial Day
17	Jul	Constitution Day
15	Aug	Independence Day
11-13	Sep	Harvest Moon Festival
3	Oct	National Foundation Day
25	Dec	Christmas

SPAIN

1	Jan	New Year's Day
6	Jan	Epiphany
21	Apr	Holy Thursday
22	Apr	Good Friday
24	Apr	Easter
1	May	Labor Day
15	Aug	Assumption
12	Oct	National Day
1	Nov	All Saints' Day
6	Dec	Constitution Day
8	Dec	Immaculate Conception
25	Dec	Christmas

SWEDEN

1	Jan	New Year's Day
5	Jan	Epiphany Eve
6	Jan	Epiphany
21	Apr	Maundy Thursday
22	Apr	Good Friday
24	Apr	Easter
25	Apr	Easter Monday
30	Apr	Walpurgis Eve
		King's Birthday
1	May	May Day
1	Jun	Day Before Ascension
2	Jun	Ascension Day
6	Jun	National Day
12	Jun	Pentecost
24	Jun	Midsummer Eve
25	Jun	Midsummer Day
4	Nov	All Saints' Eve
5	Nov	All Saints' Day
24	Dec	Christmas Eve
25	Dec	Christmas
26	Dec	Boxing Day
31	Dec	New Year's Eve

SWITZERLAND

1	Jan	New Year's Day
22	Apr	Good Friday
24	Apr	Easter
25	Apr	Easter Monday
2	Jun	Ascension Day
12	Jun	Pentecost
13	Jun	Whit Monday
1	Aug	National Day
25	Dec	Christmas

THAILAND

1	Jan	New Year's Day
18	Feb	Makha Bucha Day
6	Apr	Chakri Day
13-15	Apr	Songkran (Thai New Year)
1	May	Labor Day
5	May	Coronation Day
17	May	Visakha Bucha Day (Buddha's Birthday)
15	Jul	Asanha Bucha Day
16	Jul	Khao Phansa (Buddhist Lent begins)
12	Aug	Queen's Birthday
23	Oct	Chulalongkorn Day
10	Nov	Loy Kratong
5	Dec	King's Birthday
10	Dec	Constitution Day
31	Dec	New Year's Eve

WORLD TIME ZONE MAP

This map is based on Coordinated Universal Time (UTC), the worldwide system of civil timekeeping. UTC is essentially equivalent to Greenwich Mean Time. Zone boundaries are approximate and subject to change. Time differences relative to UTC shown here are based on the use of standard time; where Daylight Saving Time (Summer Time) is employed, add one hour to local standard time.

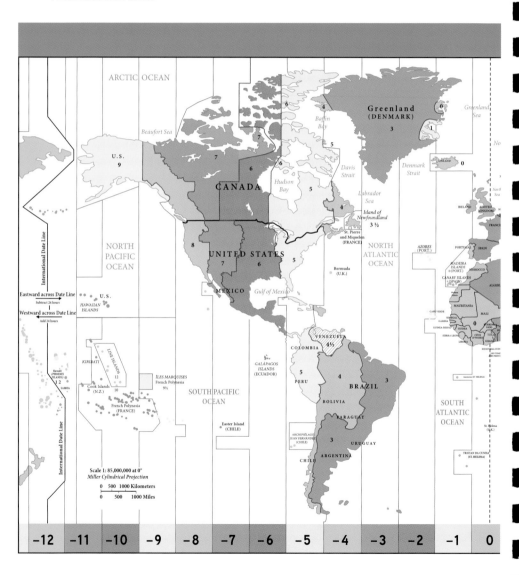

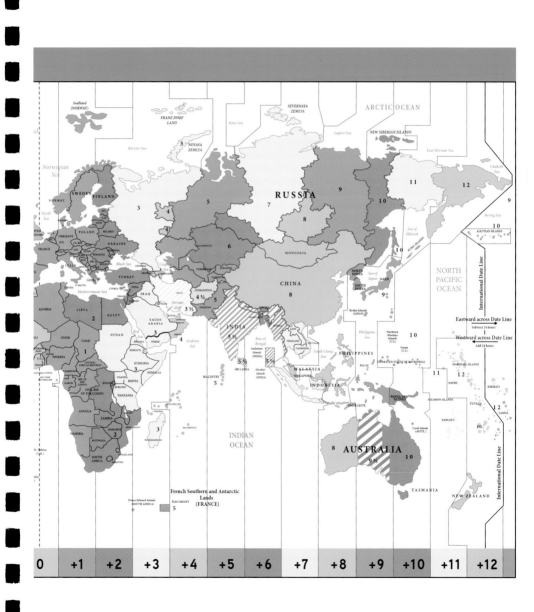

Svalbard (NORWAY)

FRANZ JOSEF LAND

SEVERNAYA ZEMLYA

ARCTIC OCEAN

Barents Sea

Kara Sea

NOVAYA ZEMLYA

Laptev Sea

NEW SIBERIAN ISLANDS

East Siberian Sea

Norwegian Sea

SWEDEN

FINLAND

North

NORWAY

Chukchi Sea

RUSSIA

11

12

9

10

9

Bering Sea

ALEUTIAN ISLANDS

10

Sea of Okhotsk

UNITED KINGDOM

GERMANY

POLAND

LIT.

LAT.

EST.

BELARUS

FRANCE

UKRAINE

KAZAKHSTAN

6

MONGOLIA

KURIL ISLANDS

10

ITALY

Black Sea

TURKEY

GEORGIA

Caspian Sea

UZBEKISTAN

KYRGYZSTAN

NORTH KOREA

Sea of Japan

JAPAN

NORTH PACIFIC OCEAN

Mediterranean Sea

CYPRUS

SYRIA

IRAQ

IRAN

AFGHANISTAN

CHINA

8

SOUTH KOREA

9

Ryukyu Islands (JAPAN)

ALGERIA

LIBYA

2

EGYPT

SAUDI ARABIA

QATAR

Persian Gulf

3½

4½

PAKISTAN

NEPAL

Philippine Sea

Northern Mariana Islands (U.S.)

10

International Date Line

NIGER

CHAD

SUDAN

ERITREA

YEMEN

OMAN

4

Arabian Sea

INDIA

5½

Bay of Bengal

THAILAND

LAOS

CAMBODIA

South China Sea

PHILIPPINES

Guam (U.S.)

Eastward across Date Line

Subtract 24 hours

Westward across Date Line

Add 24 hours

NIGERIA

CENTRAL AFRICAN REPUBLIC

1

ETHIOPIA

SOMALIA

3

MALDIVES

5½

SRI LANKA

Andaman Islands (INDIA)

Nicobar Islands (INDIA)

5½

MALAYSIA

SINGAPORE

FEDERATED STATES OF MICRONESIA

PALAU

MARSHALL ISLANDS

11

12

GABON

DEM. REP. OF THE CONGO

UGANDA

KENYA

BURUNDI

RWANDA

TANZANIA

SEYCHELLES

INDONESIA

PAPUA NEW GUINEA

TIMOR-LESTE

NAURU

KIRIBATI

ANGOLA

ZAMBIA

ZIMBABWE

3

COMOROS

MAURITIUS

INDIAN OCEAN

Coral Islands (AUSTL.)

SOLOMON ISLANDS

TUVALU

12

NAMIBIA

BOTSWANA

2

MADAGASCAR

8

AUSTRALIA

9½

10

VANUATU

PHJI.

St. Helena (U.K.)

SOUTH AFRICA

SWAZILAND

LESOTHO

Prince Edward Islands (SOUTH AFRICA)

ÎLES CROZET

5

French Southern and Antarctic Lands (FRANCE)

TASMANIA

NEW ZEALAND

International Date Line

| 0 | +1 | +2 | +3 | +4 | +5 | +6 | +7 | +8 | +9 | +10 | +11 | +12 |

2012

JANUARY

s	m	t	w	t	f	s
1	2	3	4	5	6	7
8	9	10	11	12	13	14
15	16	17	18	19	20	21
22	23	24	25	26	27	28
29	30	31				

FEBRUARY

s	m	t	w	t	f	s
			1	2	3	4
5	6	7	8	9	10	11
12	13	14	15	16	17	18
19	20	21	22	23	24	25
26	27	28	29			

MARCH

s	m	t	w	t	f	s
				1	2	3
4	5	6	7	8	9	10
11	12	13	14	15	16	17
18	19	20	21	22	23	24
25	26	27	28	29	30	31

APRIL

s	m	t	w	t	f	s
1	2	3	4	5	6	7
8	9	10	11	12	13	14
15	16	17	18	19	20	21
22	23	24	25	26	27	28
29	30					

MAY

s	m	t	w	t	f	s
		1	2	3	4	5
6	7	8	9	10	11	12
13	14	15	16	17	18	19
20	21	22	23	24	25	26
27	28	29	30	31		

JUNE

s	m	t	w	t	f	s
					1	2
3	4	5	6	7	8	9
10	11	12	13	14	15	16
17	18	19	20	21	22	23
24	25	26	27	28	29	30

2012

JULY

s	m	t	w	t	f	s
1	2	3	4	5	6	7
8	9	10	11	12	13	14
15	16	17	18	19	20	21
22	23	24	25	26	27	28
29	30	31				

AUGUST

s	m	t	w	t	f	s
			1	2	3	4
5	6	7	8	9	10	11
12	13	14	15	16	17	18
19	20	21	22	23	24	25
26	27	28	29	30	31	

SEPTEMBER

s	m	t	w	t	f	s
						1
2	3	4	5	6	7	8
9	10	11	12	13	14	15
16	17	18	19	20	21	22
23	24	25	26	27	28	29
30						

OCTOBER

s	m	t	w	t	f	s
	1	2	3	4	5	6
7	8	9	10	11	12	13
14	15	16	17	18	19	20
21	22	23	24	25	26	27
28	29	30	31			

NOVEMBER

s	m	t	w	t	f	s
				1	2	3
4	5	6	7	8	9	10
11	12	13	14	15	16	17
18	19	20	21	22	23	24
25	26	27	28	29	30	

DECEMBER

s	m	t	w	t	f	s
						1
2	3	4	5	6	7	8
9	10	11	12	13	14	15
16	17	18	19	20	21	22
23	24	25	26	27	28	29
30	31					

2012 YEAR PLANNER

	JANUARY	FEBRUARY	MARCH
1	s — New Year's Day	w	th
2	m — **New Year's Day holiday** Bank Holiday (Canada, UK)	th	f
3	t — Bank Holiday (Scotland)	f	s
4	w	s	s
5	th	s	m
6	f	m	t
7	s	t	w — Purim (begins at sunset)
8	s	w	th — International Women's Day
9	m	th	f
10	t	f	s
11	w	s	s — Daylight Saving Time begins
12	th	s	m
13	f	m	t
14	s	t — Valentine's Day	w
15	s	w	th
16	m — **Martin Luther King Jr. Day**	th	f
17	t	f	s — St. Patrick's Day
18	w	s	s — Mothering Sunday (UK)
19	th	s	m
20	f	m — **Presidents' Day**	t — Vernal Equinox 05:14 UTC
21	s	t — Mardi Gras	w
22	s	w — Ash Wednesday	th
23	m — Lunar New Year	th	f
24	t	f	s
25	w	s	s — Summer Time begins (UK)
26	th	s	m
27	f	m	t
28	s	t	w
29	s	w	th
30	m		f
31	t		s

2012 YEAR PLANNER

	APRIL	MAY	JUNE
1	s — Palm Sunday	t	f
2	m	w	s
3	t	th	s
4	w	f	m
5	th	s — Cinco de Mayo	t
6	f — Good Friday—Passover (begins at sunset)—Bank Holiday (Canada, UK)	s	w
7	s	m — Bank Holiday (UK)	th
8	s — Easter	t	f
9	m — Easter Monday (Canada, UK except Scotland)	w	s
10	t	th	s
11	w	f	m
12	th	s	t
13	f	s — Mother's Day	w
14	s	m	th — Flag Day
15	s	t	f
16	m	w	s
17	t	th	s — Father's Day
18	w	f	m
19	th	s — Armed Forces Day	t
20	f	s	w — Summer Solstice 23:09 UTC
21	s	m — Victoria Day (Canada)	th
22	s — Earth Day	t	f
23	m	w	s
24	t	th	s
25	w	f	m
26	th	s	t
27	f	s	w
28	s	m — **Memorial Day** / Bank Holiday (UK)	th
29	s	t	f
30	m	w	s
31		th	

2012 YEAR PLANNER

	JULY	AUGUST	SEPTEMBER
1	s — Canada Day (Canada)	w	s
2	m — Canada Day holiday (Canada)	th	s
3	t	f	m — **Labor Day (US, Canada)**
4	w — **Independence Day**	s	t
5	th	s	w
6	f	m — Civic Holiday (Canada, most provinces) / Bank Holiday (Scotland)	th
7	s	t	f
8	s	w	s
9	m	th	s
10	t	f	m
11	w	s	t
12	th — Bank Holiday (N. Ireland)	s	w
13	f	m	th
14	s	t	f
15	s	w	s
16	m	th	s — Rosh Hashanah (begins at sunset)
17	t	f	m
18	w	s	t
19	th	s	w
20	f	m	th
21	s	t	f — International Day of Peace
22	s	w	s — Autumnal Equinox 14:49 UTC
23	m	th	s
24	t	f	m
25	w	s	t — Yom Kippur (begins at sunset)
26	th	s	w
27	f	m — Bank Holiday (UK except Scotland)	th
28	s	t	f
29	s	w	s
30	m	th	s
31	t	f	

2012 YEAR PLANNER

	OCTOBER	NOVEMBER	DECEMBER
1	m	th	s
2	t	f	s
3	w	s	m
4	th	s Daylight Saving Time ends	t
5	f	m	w
6	s	t Election Day	th
7	s	w	f
8	m **Columbus Day** Thanksgiving Day (Canada)	th	s Hanukkah (begins at sunset)
9	t	f	s
10	w	s	m
11	th	s Veterans Day Remembrance Day (Canada)	t
12	f	m **Veterans Day holiday**	w
13	s	t	th
14	s	w	f
15	m	th	s
16	t	f	s
17	w	s	m
18	th	s	t
19	f	m	w
20	s	t	th
21	s	w	f Winter Solstice 11:11 UTC
22	m	th **Thanksgiving**	s
23	t	f	s
24	w United Nations Day	s	m
25	th	s	t **Christmas**
26	f	m	w Kwanzaa begins Boxing Day (Canada, UK)
27	s	t	th
28	s Summer Time ends (UK)	w	f
29	m	th	s
30	t	f St. Andrew's Day (Scotland)	s
31	w Halloween		m

Notes

Notes

Personal Information

name _____

address _____

city _____ state _____ zip _____

phone _____

cell/pgr _____ fax _____

e-mail _____

in case of emergency, please notify:

name _____

address _____

city _____ state _____ zip _____

phone _____

physician's name _____

physician's phone _____

health insurance company _____

plan number _____

allergies _____

other _____

driver's license number _____

car insurance company _____

policy number _____